Say the sounds and blend them together to read the words.

Look at the letters and say the sounds. See how quickly you can say all of them.

v

z g

j ai

b

ee

or f

Say the word *boot* and listen out for the sounds: *boot* – /b-oo-t/. (There is one sound dot underneath the boot for each sound in the word.)